The Roots of Leadership

Anthony C. Gruppo and Karen Mayo
with Friends

Dear Dylan,

lots of happiness
always!

Cheers to your
greatness!!

Karen

ISBN: 10:0-9991471-0-2
ISBN: 13:978-0-9991471-0-8

Special acknowledgments to:

Senior Editor: Nina C. Helms

Public Creations Team:

    Michelle Foschino   Caryn Ojeda   Nick Vrouvas

The Roots of Leadership

Anthony C. Gruppo and Karen Mayo
with Friends

The Roots of Leadership is a journal which provides motivational quotes and reflective suggestions. It is a guide for you to explore the roots of leadership in order to establish a personal leadership and life plan.

Journaling has an ancient history, one that dates back to as early as the 10th century. Many successful people throughout history have kept a journal. The benefits of journaling have been well documented. Here are a few to consider as you begin journaling using The Roots of Leadership:

- Strengthen thoughts and harness emotions.
- Increase emotional intelligence.
- Improve self-discipline.
- Enhance communication skills.
- Develop deeper self-understanding.
- Create stronger solutions and innovative ideas.
- Reduce stress and increase energy.

The Roots of Leadership is a platform for you to enter deep into your strengths to reach your higher potential. We invite you to journal your personal guide to greatness. Regardless of our role in life, we are all leaders. Within the roots of our leadership, diversity is the unique system we each possess.

May your journal become the generational documentation to serve as a testimony to the example you set for those to come.

Enjoy the journey,

Leadership is walking into a room with
an air of vulnerability and humility,
and yet a look in your eyes of undeniable courage.

- Anthony C. Gruppo

Achievers and believers have a common love.
The love of the game. Take on all comers. Just believe.

- Anthony C. Gruppo

Reflect: How would you describe your love of the game?

Like the metamorphosis of a butterfly, change takes time.

- Stephanie Caulo

Do not be scared to be weird, awkward or crazy.
Be yourself and you will find your place.

- Juliana No

Authenticity cannot be masked, changed, or faked.
Be true to yourself and everyone you meet.

- Chantal Raineri

When you walk on the edge, it may scare others.
Have faith in your ability and push past your limits every day.

- Tomaso Rotondi

Reflect: What are some areas in your life where you could be walking on the edge? What is holding you back?

It is the fearful and the ignorant who judge
what is right and what is wrong.
Letting go of judgment = peace of mind.

- Nina C. Helms

Interrupt a part of your routine.
Disrupt what is usually commonplace.
You will create sparks to fire up your momentum.

- Anthony C. Gruppo

Reflect: Identify a disruptor that might challenge you in the future. How will you adjust?

The light of leadership will be forever bright
if we help others shine.

- Anthony C. Gruppo

Reflect: Who did you help obtain a success?
What was the result?

Communication is the compass to find
the road to a caring culture.

- Karen Mayo

Reflect: How can you clarify communication with your teams?

Wherever we stand is our playground.
Whatever we dream is our game.

- Anthony C. Gruppo

Reflect: What is fun about your work?
How can you make it fun for others?

So many thoughts flying around in your head.
You feel like you are not effective.
Congratulations, you are a visionary!
Grab one thought and go.

- Anthony C. Gruppo

Reflect: Write down one wild idea and act on it.

Think of someone who has impacted your life, let them know. It may be just what they need to hear today.

- Caryn Ojeda

You can monitor a leader's pulse rate by goals per minute.

- Anthony C. Gruppo

Reflect: What is the first goal that comes to your mind? When will you complete it? What are the intended results?

You do not pursue money, you pursue dreams,
and then they pay you for it. It is that simple.

- Anthony C. Gruppo

Reflect: Consider becoming a donor to a
not-for-profit organization.

Carve out time for creative thinking.
New ideas have no expiration dates.

- Anthony C. Gruppo

Reflect: Schedule time in your calendar for creative thinking.

The promise of a better tomorrow lies within your heart today.

- Anthony C. Gruppo

Reflect: You have many decisions to make every day.
Focus on how you handle one. Observe your emotions.
How do you approach the most difficult ones?

Our world has been created to perfection.
Every creature has a purpose. Embrace who you are.
You have a greater purpose beyond the obvious.

- Dawn Damatta

Mindful eating is eating with awareness of
how the food is making you feel.

- Karen Mayo

Reflect: Has what you put into your body served you well
today?

It is not what you will get out of an experience,
it is about what you will become because of it.

- Tomaso Rotondi

Reflect: Take a moment after each new experience to understand the changes that were realized.

Use mindful meditation to be mindful of the
focus you need to achieve.

- Anthony C. Gruppo

Reflect: Write down one uncompleted task you will focus on
achieving tomorrow morning.

Your future is formed by your present creations.

- Anthony C. Gruppo

Reflect: Use your hands to create a piece of artwork.
Even if it is coloring with a child using crayons.

Create inner space for self-love and healing.
Life is imbalanced if we only work and energize the external.

- Nina C. Helms

Never alter your soul or mind to conform to the environment.
Adjust the environment to align with your heart, mind and soul.

- Daphne Steele

So much fun to outlast your last failure. Go chase a dream.

- Anthony C. Gruppo

A well-balanced leader possesses equal parts
energy and self-control.

- Anthony C. Gruppo

Vision is an ever-changing landscape.
Moving with some uncertainty is the excitement.

- Anthony C. Gruppo

Reflect: Outline your long-term vision.
How are you preparing for it?

Weary from the weight of challenge? Lift yourself by knowing your strength is the ticket to the competition.

- Anthony C. Gruppo

Reflect: Which three strengths do you consistently utilize?

Live inside out. Take the courage you have inside of you and bring it out to strengthen those you love and serve.

- Anthony C. Gruppo

Be someone's Comfort Zone.

- Anthony C. Gruppo

Reflect: What does this mean to you? Who comes to mind? How can you comfort them?

A positive thinker knows a setback
merely changes the timing of the impossible.

- Anthony C. Gruppo

Reflect: What appears impossible to you?
What is a setback you overcame?

If you are amazed at how badly someone treats you, perhaps you should be even more amazed why you allow it.

- Tim Fargo

We are a force of one in a team of many.

- Anthony C. Gruppo

Reflect: How will you stand out without showing ego?

A mother's <u>MOM</u>entum can sustain a family for generations.

- Anthony C. Gruppo

Reflect: What is one thing you learned
from Mom you use often?

Mental and physical toughness smooth out the rough road.

- Anthony C. Gruppo

Reflect: How will you add more strength into your life?
Call someone and encourage them.

If you feel smothered by pressure, know you are
the breath of fresh air for those who count on you.

- Anthony C. Gruppo

Selfless mentoring is an insurance policy
protecting a culture from chaos.

- Anthony C. Gruppo

Reflect: Take a new colleague to lunch this week and
share a valuable lesson you have learned.

What would you do if you did not have goals
to wake up to each day? They breathe passion into us.

- Anthony C. Gruppo

Reflect: Rewrite a goal statement and rate it from 1 to 5
based on your confidence for completion.

Consistent positive behavior from leadership
creates consistent results for those whom they serve.

- Anthony C. Gruppo

Reflect: List two results which helped others because
you stayed positive when others had doubts.

Personal mission and vision are threads
to sew our motivational quilt.

- Anthony C. Gruppo

Reflect: Write your personal mission statement.
Who is the first person you will share it with?

Forward movement. Forward movement always.

- Susan Durando

It is our imperfections which create our uniqueness.
Perfect is so boring. Use your imperfections
to create the amazing.

- Anthony C. Gruppo

Reflect: What are two flaws you used to your advantage to create a positive outcome?

If you are struggling in a relationship,
pause to create a positive future vision for that person.

- Jennifer Davis

Reflect: How will you help someone to be more positive?

If an olive branch is extended, reach out and take it,
even if it is not exactly what you wanted.

- Jennifer Davis

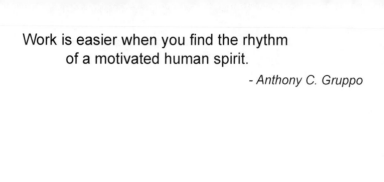

Work is easier when you find the rhythm
of a motivated human spirit.

- Anthony C. Gruppo

Reflect: Arrive at work one hour earlier for the next five days.

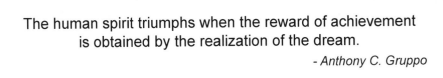

The human spirit triumphs when the reward of achievement
is obtained by the realization of the dream.

- Anthony C. Gruppo

Reflect: What is a dream of yours? Where will you start?
Who have you told about it?

If we refuse to increase our personal drive and motivational system, we risk suffocating in our own Comfort Zone.

- Anthony C. Gruppo

Reflect: How will you challenge yourself?

Self-awareness is the ability to look at oneself
with an unfiltered perception.

- Peggy McGrane

How will you have a positive impact on someone's attitude?

- Anthony C. Gruppo

Reflect: Think of a person who is negative.
How can you help them to have a positive impact?

The essence of a leader is a mediator with both
the mind of a facilitator and the heart of a negotiator.

- Anthony C. Gruppo

Reflect: Think of what emotions you often use
to obtain results.

Self-doubt is often caused by the insecurities of others.
Believe in yourself.

- Anthony C. Gruppo

Reflect: Is there someone holding you back?
What will you do about it?

Diversity gives us the power
to be better equipped to handle adversity.

- Anthony C. Gruppo

Reflect: What is diverse about your mindset?

The motivated are not judgmental.
They see charm where others see nonconformity.

- Anthony C. Gruppo

Reflect: Have you judged anyone without knowing
the root cause?

A diverse leadership team can write the music
for everyone they serve. Dance your way to greatness.

- Anthony C. Gruppo

Reflect: How has diversity made you stronger?

Be visible. Refuse to blend in.
Strengthen someone who has retreated into the shadows.

- Anthony C. Gruppo

Reflect: How have you helped someone to gain confidence?

Strengthening a relationship today,
builds a stronger leader tomorrow.

- Anthony C. Gruppo

Reflect: If you had to enhance one relationship by the
end of day, where would you start?

When planning your production season,
make the time to learn what foods are in season.

- Karen Mayo

Reflect: Research foods in season.
How will you use them in your meal plan?

A personal strategic plan is only limited by its builder. Your vision is the foundation of the plan.

- John Sames

Reflect: What limits you from implementing your personal strategic plan?

You are a work in progress. Change will be constant, fear will be fleeting, doubt will be erased and success will be yours.

- Anthony C. Gruppo

Reflect: If you were to hire a performance coach, where would you want them to start?

Fitness of mind and body is how to de-stress for success.

- Karen Mayo

Reflect: How do you effectively deal with stress?

Be who others trust when things go wrong.

- Anthony C. Gruppo

Reflect: When was the last time someone came to you?
What was the result?

Engage colleagues' opinions and advice in areas
other than their jobs. Their insights improve your vision.

- Anthony C. Gruppo

Reflect: What are three areas you would feel comfortable in
seeking a colleague's opinion?

A father's servant leadership can guide a family's future.

- Anthony C. Gruppo

Reflect: What does fatherhood mean to you?

Harmony is a state of mind, which expands its borders
when shared with others.

- Anthony C. Gruppo

Reflect: How do you keep a harmonious balance?

Let us not stay because of the success of yesterday or the thrill of today. Let us stay for the dreams of tomorrow.

- Anthony C. Gruppo

Reflect: What skills do you need to develop to become more competitive?

Have as your goal to be an experienced architect in the constructing of your personal potential.

- Anthony C. Gruppo

Reflect: What percentage of your maximum potential have you reached?

If textbook methods fail, seek out a
street smart fighter with raw passion to enter the challenge.

- Anthony C. Gruppo

Reflect: What are you passionate about?
Do others know what it is?

Without perpetuation and succession planning,
the culture cracks and the future blurs.

- Anthony C. Gruppo

Reflect: What traits would you want your successor
to possess?

Create a positive affirmation about yourself;
say it if your confidence dips.

- Anthony C. Gruppo

Reflect: Write a positive affirmation and share it
with someone.

Spend less time being offended by others and
more time defending others.

- Sandra Tailor

Reflect: When was the last time you stood up for someone?

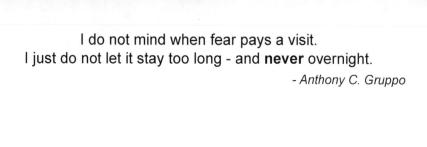

I do not mind when fear pays a visit.
I just do not let it stay too long - and **never** overnight.

- Anthony C. Gruppo

Reflect: What technique do you use to reduce fear?

The teachers of vision have the future as their student.

- Anthony C. Gruppo

Reflect: Who do you want to mentor?
Set up a time to talk about the possibility.

If your vision is often directed to your smart device,
can you ever devise a smart vision?

- Karen Mayo

Reflect: What is your personal vision statement?

When the pressure gets to you, when you feel like quitting;
walk in the rain, feel the wind, journal a thought.
Make a comeback.

- Anthony C. Gruppo

Reflect: How do you release pressure?
Is it a short or long-term solution?

When we add play time, we add more productive results to work time.

- Karen Mayo

Empowerment is an inheritance received from those who made sacrifices before you. Pass it on to others.

- Anthony C. Gruppo

Reflect: Ask someone to do a task you always do yourself.

As leaders, we rent our positions. Let us leave it with upgrades and renovations for the new leader to occupy.

- Anthony C. Gruppo

Reflect: Write the name of your replacement if you left tomorrow.

Selflessness is an exceptional quality.
However, being selfish in the name of self-care is also
a gift you give to those you care for.

- Nina C. Helms

Reflect: Do a practice or activity today that supports your
body, soul and your health.

Everyone is constantly under construction.
Build upon your vision to achieve the impossible.

- Anthony C. Gruppo

Reflect: What does being under construction mean to you?

Preparation is the laboratory where opportunities are invented.

- Anthony C. Gruppo

Reflect: What are two components you always include
when preparing for an opportunity?

Do not seek to be clever, work to be competent.

- Anthony C. Gruppo

Do not make it complicated. Build the plan, sell the plan, execute the plan. Make mistakes, laugh at yourself, get back in there. Repeat.

- Anthony C. Gruppo

Reflect: Write the opening paragraph for your personal business plan.

Healthy snacks during the day prevent a boardroom
from becoming a bored room.

- Karen Mayo

Reflect: Prepare healthy snacks to carry with you.

Exercising the body + Exercising the mind =
Positive Mind and Body.

- Karen Mayo

Reflect: What will you do today to achieve a
positive mind and body?

We are walking, talking, eating, drinking and breathing filtration systems.

- Karen Mayo

Facing a physical challenge can help you to face and conquer deep emotional fears. Try it!

- Jennifer Davis

An unhealthy meal today can inhibit productivity tomorrow.

- Karen Mayo

Reflect: What causes you to eat an unhealthy meal?

Education is a long-term investment that needs no refund.

- Jennifer Turner

The best education does not prepare students for a test, college, or a job. It prepares them to keep learning.

- Danny Steele

Look for the courage it takes to continue to push forward and stay focused when the tide is against you.

- Anthony C. Gruppo

Reflect: Who do you know who is courageous?
What do you admire about them?

Unconditionally step up and step in for someone
who needs help.
Be the reason amazing happens for others.

- Anthony C. Gruppo

Reflect: Who comes to mind needing your help?
What can you do for them?

Make a promise to move with a purpose. Be amazing.

- Anthony C. Gruppo

Reflect: What will you achieve this week that will
inspire others?

Treat everyone you meet as if they are the most important person in the world, because to someone they are.

- Dawn Damatta

Standing humble at the threshold of a challenge
opens the door to being successful.

- Anthony C. Gruppo

Reflect: How would others define your humility?

Facing a challenge is similar to tight rope walking.
One goal in front of the other, as you take
steps toward your vision.

- Anthony C. Gruppo

Reflect: State one of your short-term and long-term goals.

You did your best today. Forget today and focus your thoughts on tomorrow. You are strong and driven.

- Anthony C. Gruppo

Reflect: What technique do you use to increase your focus?

Your job title is temporary - what you achieve with it
is permanent.

- Anthony C. Gruppo

Reflect: Does your title accurately identify
your responsibilities?

You can set the example which will generate greatness for generations.

- Anthony C. Gruppo

Reflect: How would you like to be remembered?

Get more sleep tonight and be wide awake for your goals tomorrow.

- Karen Mayo

Reflect: Go to bed thirty minutes earlier tonight.

When you make a name for yourself, do not forget the names of those who helped you.

- Anthony C. Gruppo

Reflect: Name five people who helped to you achieve your goals.

When we see the best in others, the best in us grows stronger.

- Anthony C. Gruppo

When the road to achievement feels too long,
know the success at the end will last even longer.

- Anthony C. Gruppo

Dreamers, doers and thinkers see possibilities everywhere.

- D'Lisa Jogie

When making a decision impacting the many,
never make it to satisfy the few.

- Anthony C. Gruppo

A leader views accountability as self-reflection.

- John E. Cicchelli

When involved in conflict resolution,
it is about what is right, not who is right.

- Anthony C. Gruppo

If you listen, you will learn something.

- Juliana No

Reflect: Ask more questions and listen to what people have
to say and their reasons for saying it.

Having a daily gratitude practice grounds us, keeps us humble and helps us to build and maintain self-awareness.

- Nina C. Helms

Reflect: Name five things you are grateful for today. Try this for a week and observe what happens.

Give your time to someone who is frozen in time.
Help them to break free of the past.

- Anthony C. Gruppo

Reflect: Does anyone come to mind who could use your help?

You will never regret the risks you took to help others.

- Anthony C. Gruppo

Reflect: Write down one risk you need to take.

Those who see only their past greatness are
blind to future opportunities.

- Anthony C. Gruppo

Approach the usual from an unusual viewpoint.
Change it up. Create newness to the routine.

- Anthony C. Gruppo

Reflect: How can you modify your routine?

Focus on all of your amazing qualities.

- Anthony C. Gruppo

Reflect: List 5 qualities you are proud of.

The space between your greatest failure and your greatest triumph is where you will be tested.

- Anthony C. Gruppo

The smallest gestures can have the largest impact.
They create consistent positive delivery.

- Anthony C. Gruppo

Reflect: What small gesture will you make for someone?

Enter situations where you can help people less fortunate. True motivation will follow for you and them.

- Anthony C. Gruppo

Fear is the total of lost moments.

- Anthony C. Gruppo

Reflect: In your life, are there lost moments you still think
about? Are they holding you back?

When you feel inspired, the ability to inspire comes
before your words are uttered.

- Anthony C. Gruppo

Leadership is taking your primary skill package and developing it to your full potential.

- Anthony C. Gruppo

Reflect: What are three of your primary skills?

Be constructive in your actions and supportive in your delivery.

- Anthony C. Gruppo

What is a soul if not the spiritual home where
our past loved ones reside?

- Anthony C. Gruppo

Always stay true to yourself and put your values first.
They define who you are.

- Juliana No

New ideas are vitamins for the mind.

- Karen Mayo

The strong understand forgiveness creates
new opportunities to grow.

- Anthony C. Gruppo

Leading tightly and tensely constricts the flow of creativity for the team.

- Anthony C. Gruppo

Leadership is giving someone a new challenge when they are not completely ready.

- Anthony C. Gruppo

You can choose to use your voice to make the world a more beautiful place, and you do not even have to sing.

- Anne Scottlin

Forgiveness is opening the door to let someone free and realizing you were the prisoner.

- Lauri D. Meizer

Leadership is knowing you are a work in progress while trying to bring progress to those you serve.

- Anthony C. Gruppo

"I look forward to" or "I can't wait to" is a great way to set up for any task, mission, meeting or to do. Self-inspire.

- Nina C. Helms

Reflect: Apply "I look forward to" vs. "I have to" before your checklist today and observe what happens.

Ten diverse minds will usually generate more creativity then one hundred like-minded. Diversity is energy.

- Anthony C. Gruppo

Respect is the thread of humanity
which sews together our fabric of greatness.

- Anthony C. Gruppo

Be understanding when others feel misunderstood.
Stand for those who cannot stand for themselves.

- Anthony C. Gruppo

Reflect: Who comes to mind needing your strength
and support?

A healthy dining plan will enhance your business plan.

- Karen Mayo

Reflect: Plan a healthy meal, shop with a family member and cook together.

Mindful eating is awareness of health.
Self-Awareness = Mindful Decisions.

- Karen Mayo

Reflect: Plan your next dinner meeting at
a healthy restaurant.

Eliminate the sugar if you want to have the energy
to sweeten the deal.

- Karen Mayo

Reflect: Take all the sugar out of your daily routine
for one day.

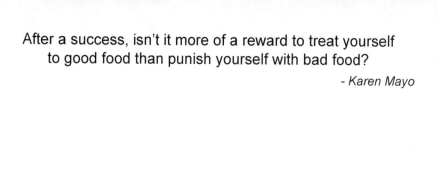

After a success, isn't it more of a reward to treat yourself
to good food than punish yourself with bad food?

- Karen Mayo

Reflect: Treat yourself to something nourishing.

The building blocks of good nutrition are the same for leadership – common sense, good judgment, discipline.

- Jennifer Turner

Super-foods will help you have super results.

- Karen Mayo

Reflect: Challenge yourself to learn two new super-foods a week.

Be a force of focused energy by eating foods which create energy.

- Karen Mayo

Reflect: Use a food tracking application for the remainder of this journaling journey.

Yoga will help you find the edge,
the edge where your mind knows no boundary.

- *Nina C. Helms*

Reflect: What edge can you safely and confidently push
this week to expand your boundaries?

Building a healthy lifestyle is making transformational baby steps.

- Karen Mayo

Reflect: What efforts can you make toward living a long healthy life?

It is simple: positive thinking and action leads to a better life. Not an easy life, but a better life.

- Tomaso Rotondi

The groundwork for success is envisioning the path forward. Believe in yourself no matter the odds.

- *Guilherme Debarros*

Self-care is taking a time out for you. Go ahead, do it!
Check your schedule right now for yourself.

- Karen Mayo

The ladder we chose to climb is as important as
the surface it stands upon.

- Linda Delorio

In matter of the mind or soul, do not go deep sea diving with someone who cannot swim.

- Rebecca Bardess

A drop in your blood sugar is a drop in your productivity.
Eat a healthy snack to elevate and succeed.

- Karen Mayo

Reflect: Grab an apple or carrots and hummus
for a perfect snack.

Sometimes our heart rate is not about exercising.
It is about exercising our heart to drive to a goal.

- Karen Mayo

Reflect: What goal are you emotionally attached to?
How is it impacting you?

Produce Lookup Codes unlock the secret to healthy eating.

- Karen Mayo

Reflect: Learn PLU (Produce Lookup Codes) Codes: 5 digit number starting with 9=organic; 4 digit number starting with 3 or 4=convention; 5 digit number starting with 8=GMO.

Create moments to design yourself into the person
whom you will be proud of.

- Brenda L. Hanley

The energy to produce results starts with avoiding bad fats.

- Karen Mayo

Reflect: How can you add the healthy fats, like nuts
and seeds, into your diet today?

Mindful eating fuels thoughtful leadership.

- Karen Mayo

Reflect: What does mindful eating mean to you?

You are not created to be "good enough."

- Bruce Van Horn

Before minimizing someone's idea, remember the energy they put into thinking of it. Motivate, do not intimidate. We are better together.

- Anthony C. Gruppo

Do not judge the next person you meet by
the last person who failed you.

- Anthony C. Gruppo

Direct communication prevents misdirected results.

- Anthony C. Gruppo

Result: What is your communication style?
Why is it effective?

When night falls and you look back over the day,
feel the image of what wonder you can create tomorrow.

- Anthony C. Gruppo

Leaders who truly care about those they serve,
breathe a rarefied air of dedication.

- Anthony C. Gruppo

Just because you are doing what you have to,
never give up doing what you want to.

- Anthony C. Gruppo

Reflect: What is something you want to do?
How will you make it happen?

Persistence is a human art form.
It is the canvas for future success.

- JoEllen Donner

Make today matter to those who matter to you.

- Anthony C. Gruppo

You could have been anyone at all,
fortunately you chose to be you.

- Anthony C. Gruppo

Someday is not a day of the week.
Make today the day you achieve a result
you have been chasing this week.

- Anthony C. Gruppo

The challenges of the future are achievable because of your past experiences.

- Anthony C. Gruppo

Reflection is the art of exercising the mind.

- Angela Minutaglio

The humble are unsure of themselves, while
the arrogant are unsure of others.

- Anthony C. Gruppo

The more fit a leader becomes, the more fit they are to lead.

- Karen Mayo

Reflect: Fast walk today for 15 minutes to
increase your heart rate.

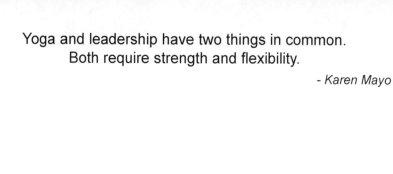

Yoga and leadership have two things in common.
Both require strength and flexibility.

- Karen Mayo

Reflect: What about you demonstrates flexibility?

Energy comes from the nourishing foods we eat and
the challenges we attempt to digest.

- Karen Mayo

Reflect: Consider fasting as a challenge.

Exercise produces the energy and fitness
to run a business.

- Karen Mayo

Reflect: What type of exercise enhances your energy?

Have an endless fascination about your future possibilities.

- Chantal Raineri

Positive affirmations create positive attitudes.

- Karen Mayo

Reflect: Together with your team create positive affirmations.

Your body of work improves when you work your body.

- Karen Mayo

Reflect: Consider treating yourself to a training session
with a nutritionist or coach.

The more sacrifices, the more achievement.

- Anthony C. Gruppo

Reflect: What sacrifice did you make and
what was the outcome?

The prepared never fear failure, they simply outwork the barrier and build a new bridge to success.

- Anthony C. Gruppo

Never fear being the lone visionary on the edge.
Lead others to believe in the impossible.

- Anthony C. Gruppo

There is nothing average about you. Go after your goals at an above average pace. You were built for this.

- Anthony C. Gruppo

The true power of your position is
how you use it to empower others.

- Anthony C. Gruppo

There are two types of listeners. Those who hear what you say and those who only hear what they want.

- Anthony C. Gruppo

There is nothing impossible about
doing the best we can for whom we serve.

- Anthony C. Gruppo

Have a positive impact on someone's attitude.

- Anthony C. Gruppo

Define your momentum not based on the day of the week,
but by the energy you bring into every moment.

- Anthony C. Gruppo

If we do not teach to the heart,
we will never reach the mind.

- Lyon Terry

Quieting your mind through meditation
connects you to your intuition.

- Sharon Werner

What is critical to your success is not being critical of others.

- Anthony C. Gruppo

What matters most to you? What are you doing about it?

- Anthony C. Gruppo

Standing alone to do the right thing will eventually
form a crowd to honor your result.

- Anthony C. Gruppo

The secret to leadership is living in the present,
while envisioning the future.

- Anthony C. Gruppo

Reflect: What do you need to let go of that is getting in
the way of your success?

Overthinking an opportunity can cause under-achievement.
Make a plan. Set the course. Go!

- Anthony C. Gruppo

Children set an example of continuous learning.
Let us, as adults, follow their lead.

- Michelle Foschino

Your potential and personality will create
moments of momentum which will last for a lifetime.

- Anthony C. Gruppo

Reflect: What three personality traits do you bring to
challenging situations to rise above them?

Intelligence is not what you know, it is
seeking what you do not know.

- John E. Cicchelli

Achieve what you imagine.

- Anthony C. Gruppo

Reflect: Imagine yourself five years from now.
Where will you be?

Always ask for an agenda before going to any meeting. Preparation leads to productivity.

- Anthony C. Gruppo

An unchallenged present creates a complacent future.

- Anthony C. Gruppo

As the work week ends, be proud of your achievements.
You made a difference. Your intellectual capital
funds the future.

- Anthony C. Gruppo

Before the day ends, let someone know
you are proud of them.

- Anthony C. Gruppo

No one can be better than you at being you.
You have the ability to achieve your brand of greatness.

- Anthony C. Gruppo

Even if all the pieces are in place to create and motivate,
you still need one critical element -
someone who believes in you.

- Anthony C. Gruppo

You cannot achieve what you have not defined.
Never leave important conversations open-ended.

- Dawn Damatta

Expecting the worst is self-imposed chaos.

- Anthony C. Gruppo

Reflect: How will you change those worries into
encouraging positive thoughts?

Embrace adversity as an opportunity to learn.
Move quietly through adversity with
faith and belief in yourself.

- Anthony C. Gruppo

If you doubt yourself, seek someone who cares about you.
Ask why they care? Use it to refuel your passion.
One "fan" will fan your fire.

- Anthony C. Gruppo

If you feel you are not good enough, or can never be great, think again. You are better than you think. Take the risk.

- Anthony C. Gruppo

It is only in self-investment that we truly succeed;
for man is the maker of his own destiny.

- Angela Minutaglio

Be your biggest fan. There may be a time when you are the only one who believes in what you are doing.

- Tomaso Rotondi

We are taught to be the teachers. We are blessed to be a blessing. We are healed to be the healers.

- Bruce Van Horn

If you try hard, you are already ahead of most.

- Anthony C. Gruppo

Best antidote to self-isolation: making yourself vulnerable
to others. Connection cures loneliness.

- Jennifer Davis

Reflect: What is the most life-changing experience you have
had in the past 10 years? What did it teach you?

Do not change who you are to become like the others,
be who you are to stand apart from others.

- Jaci Wright

The words you speak to your children today will echo in the hearts of the generations that follow them.

- John Finch

Eat a healthy meal today and close
an amazing deal tomorrow.

- Karen Mayo

Reflect: Challenge yourself to eat cleanly for the next week.

You should know your farmer like you know your doctor.
Good health starts with good food.

- John Ubaldo

Reflect: Take time to know where your food is produced.

A nutritionist is the gatekeeper to the
ultimate executive suite of success.

- Karen Mayo

Reflect: Check in with your eating habits. Write down
everything you have eaten and drank for the past 48 hours.

Serve yourself and you eat alone,
serve others and you enjoy a banquet.

- Kevin McLaughlin

We must never lose the child within us.
Successful leaders have an inner child
who prevents them from being complacent.

- Anthony C. Gruppo

Reflect: Pick a game you played as a child
and play it this week.

Setbacks and triumphs, bliss and heartache, wrinkles and gray hair are the tapestry of our sensational lives. Regret has no home in your heart.

- Nina C. Helms

Reflect: Identify something left unforgiven and practice letting go to find forgiveness.

The man your daughter will marry is greatly influenced by
the one she sees in you.

- John Finch

Every day we win or lose.
Learn the lessons in each loss and honor the wins.

- Tomaso Rotondi

Let us not talk about someone who is not present to offer their side. We waste so much time only hearing one side.

- Anthony C. Gruppo

No one is successful without the support of others.

- Anthony C. Gruppo

Reflect: Thank your colleagues and families for the role they play in your success.

Successful negotiation comes from caring less about what you want and more about what the other party needs.

- Anthony C. Gruppo

Promoting and supporting colleagues is more important than chasing a personal job promotion.

- Anthony C. Gruppo

Those who never challenge the possibilities of tomorrow, settle for the average of today.

- Anthony C. Gruppo

Because of you, others will trust. Because of you, others will not stray from their dreams. Be the anchor of courage.

- Anthony C. Gruppo

Ever wonder what the people we mentor
say to their friends about our mentoring skills?

- Anthony C. Gruppo

Reflect: Evaluate someone you have mentored.
How are they mentoring someone else?

Those who support you breathe life into your spirit.

- Maryann Mahon

Every footprint we make is related to the path we choose.
We control our destiny on the path to greatness.

- Anthony C. Gruppo

Go to sleep proud of yourself. Wake up proud of what you have created. Be proud of those you work with.

- Anthony C. Gruppo

Never allow the pessimists to take you down into their "whine" cellar. Remain optimistic.

- Anthony C. Gruppo

Everyone wants to go home at night feeling as though they made a difference. Be the difference maker.

- Anthony C. Gruppo

Encouragement ignites potential. Encourage someone.

- Anthony C. Gruppo

Reflect: Do you see potential in someone?
Encourage them to elevate their vision.

Listening is more than nodding your head; it is hearing their heart, sensing their spirit, and absorbing their words.

- Brenda L. Hanley

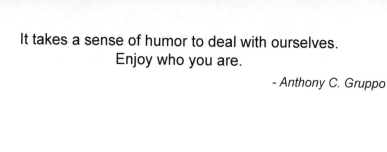

It takes a sense of humor to deal with ourselves.
Enjoy who you are.

- Anthony C. Gruppo

Reflect: When was the last time you laughed at yourself?

It is perfectly acceptable to be imperfect.
Use what you have and take action. Moving forward
versus the odds is perfection in motion.

- Anthony C. Gruppo

Effective leaders listen more and talk less.

- Anthony C. Gruppo

It is important we be honest with ourselves.
Admit our weaknesses. Do not hide them.
Work on them and move forward.

- Anthony C. Gruppo

Leaders prepare for the moment when they must break ties and make the decisions only they can make.

- Anthony C. Gruppo

Let go today the decisions you made yesterday and prepare for those you will make tomorrow.

- Anthony C. Gruppo

No matter where you sit, stand up for yourself.

- Anthony C. Gruppo

Just because you can wear it or do it,
does not mean you should.

- Juliana No

Reflect: When choosing your outfits, remember to always
dress like the person you want to be.

Recognizing the work of others is a testimony to
your humility and self-awareness.

- Anthony C. Gruppo

Diversity is not about gender or race. It is about people with different values and mindsets working together to add value to a goal.

- Juliana No

Being happy for others' good fortune is
an undeniable sign of leadership.

- Wendy Woolfork

Does your marriage include friendship?
Never lose the foundation.
Take a weekly date, be playful, romantic and fun!

- Ari Sytner

Stand beside someone and let them feel your strength.
That is all we ask of one another.

- Anthony C. Gruppo

The challenges of leadership can cause us to distance ourselves from others. Stay approachable, available and open.
Stand and deliver.

- Anthony C. Gruppo

A leader's discipline starts at the dinner table,
before they ever take a seat at the boardroom table.

- Karen Mayo

Reflect: Establish a family dinner time twice a week.

We have to trust in ourselves that we can accomplish new horizons as we stay focused on the task at hand.

- Anthony C. Gruppo

What we do today decides our tomorrow.
We are the historians of our legacy.

- Anthony C. Gruppo

Reflect: Maintain a separate journal of your successes.

When a team achieves together, there is a collateral success
that creates a potential to exceed future objectives.

- Anthony C. Gruppo

Reflect: What was your last team success?
Who were the team players? When is the next game?

When leading, share a personal story that helped you grow. Storytelling binds the motivated to the mission.

- Anthony C. Gruppo

Reflect: What personal story can you tell?

When you have passion for everything,
you rarely fear anything.

- Anthony C. Gruppo

Reflect: What are your passions?

You are a superhero. You have a super attitude.
You are someone's hero.

- Anthony C. Gruppo

Reflect: Who are your superheroes, mentors?

You are someone's motivation and inspiration.
Remember to honor the position they have given you.

- Anthony C. Gruppo

Inspiration comes from all the people with whom we interact.
Have faith in the human spirit.
Allow others to access your vision.

- Anthony C. Gruppo

Reflect: Acknowledge a colleague this week for
their vision and inspiration.

During meditation, think greatness and a great day will arise.

- Karen Mayo

Reflect: What is your message of how to achieve greatness?

Sunday is the perfect day to make random calls to friends.
Ask about their week.

- Anthony C. Gruppo

Reflect: Schedule time in your calendar to make these calls.

Do not play on the safe side of life.
You are too strong to be bored with average.

- Anthony C. Gruppo

Your future is a choice just like the past was. Own it.

- Dawn Damatta

Your future is waiting for the best of you to arrive.

- Anthony C. Gruppo

Reflect: Jot down three areas of self-development.
Make a personal contract to stay on top.

Call on yourself to answer the toughest questions
holding you back from reaching your potential.

- Anthony C. Gruppo

Reflect: What are the questions you are facing which
may create doubt?

If you feel underestimated, turn that into your art form and prove everyone wrong.

- Chantal Raineri

Closed doors are the universe's way of getting you back on the right track. Listen with your eyes wide open.

- Dawn Damatta

Choose to grow young, not to grow old.
See the opportunity over the ordeal and you will
enjoy a panoramic view of business and life.

- Anthony C. Gruppo

If you can think, care, believe and compete,
you can achieve every dream you ever conceived.

- Anthony C. Gruppo

Imagination allows us to take apart problems
and reassemble them into a plan with solutions.

- Anthony C. Gruppo

Let us mentor the children. In return, they will assist us to remember how to communicate with our inner child.

- Anthony C. Gruppo

Our spirit is our backbone when doubt starts taking control.

- Anthony C. Gruppo

The dawn of a new day is all the persuasion needed to chase a new challenge.

- Anthony C. Gruppo

Remove the training wheels of risk.
Soft peddling through life loses momentum.

- Anthony C. Gruppo

Believe that whatever falls on you tomorrow can be raised off with faith and a courageous strength of heart.

- Anthony C. Gruppo

Information is the catalyst that leads to evolution.

- Holly May Melnick

I wonder at the end of the day, when collectively we all think about how we did, if we realize we are linked by that one thought?

- Anthony C. Gruppo

In business and life, if moods manage us, our momentum is stopped. Being positive is not just a saying, it is a life catalyst.

- Anthony C. Gruppo

If a lost loved one is on your mind, remember why you loved them and seek to love someone as they loved you.

- Anthony C. Gruppo

Before developing an opinion about someone,
learn about their path and journey.

- Jeffrey Vanterpool

If not now, when? Make a bold move. You can do it.

- Anthony C. Gruppo

Upon reflection, what you perceive as reality is often merely a projection of our own expectations.

- Anne Scottlin

There is a genius sleeping inside every one of us.
Some of us have found ways to awaken it.

- Filip Slusarczyk

If we were all together this evening, talking about what inspires us and motivate us, we would leave knowing it is what lies inside of us that binds us.
The diversity of humanity is the greatest motivator.

- Anthony C. Gruppo

Inside you lies the dream.
The dream everyone who needs you has been waiting for.

- Anthony C. Gruppo

Invest in the dreams of children.
The return on investment is our leaders of tomorrow.

- Anthony C. Gruppo

Just one simple morning moment can create momentum for the day. What is your moment?

- Anthony C. Gruppo

Leadership is accepting final responsibility,
regardless of the outcome.

- Anthony C. Gruppo

Leadership is being the last one in the room
still asking if we have done enough.

- Anthony C. Gruppo

Leadership is having to tell someone they are not ready
when they believe they are.

- Anthony C. Gruppo

Leadership is motivating colleagues to care about
the mission and each other.

- Anthony C. Gruppo

Leadership is remembering colleagues names,
asking about their families and meaning it.

- Anthony C. Gruppo

Moments decide our attitude.
Use every moment to strengthen your attitude.

- Anthony C. Gruppo

People without a plan are disrupted.
People with a plan are disruptors.

- Anthony C. Gruppo

No matter what you have to face this week,
face it with class and the talent you know you possess.

- Anthony C. Gruppo

Perhaps our ultimate truth is that we are just trying to leave something worthwhile behind for others.

- Anthony C. Gruppo

If you are on the right path in life, you cannot slow down.
There are others behind you who may run you over.

- Charles Pessagno

Be deliberate about where you place your focus;
it activates outcomes that are aligned with
your vision, energy and intentions.

- Wendy Woolfork

Personal belief in oneself is the birthplace of individuality.

- Anthony C. Gruppo

Someone is watching you today with the hope of seeing an example that can help them.

- Anthony C. Gruppo

Speak to someone others just pass by. Listen to someone who is rarely heard. See those invisible to others.

- Anthony C. Gruppo

Strength is believing in yourself regardless the outcome.

- Anthony C. Gruppo

Take a chance on someone tomorrow.

- Anthony C. Gruppo

The antidote for disease of indifference is the passion to perform.

- Anthony C. Gruppo

The closest we ever come to perfect is knowing and embracing that we are not. Perfect is so boring.

- Anthony C. Gruppo

The greatest display of power is when you
do not need to use it and can still motivate others.

- Anthony C. Gruppo

The moment you become frustrated,
you have surrendered to whatever caused the frustration.

- Anthony C. Gruppo

There is something sacred about sharing your internal strength to defeat an external weakness.

- Anthony C. Gruppo

Spend more time solving problems and
less time discussing how the problems happened.

- Anthony C. Gruppo

Trying to recapture your past will hold you prisoner from enjoying your future.

- Anthony C. Gruppo

Always put people in a place to succeed:
moments are to be strived for.

- James Leeper

Unrealistic expectation can be the toughest opponent.

- Anthony C. Gruppo

Reflect: What do you expect from yourself and others?

You cannot exercise much power without gratitude;
for it is gratitude that keeps you connected with power.

- Bruce Van Horn

In the face of adversity, your character and mental toughness will determine the success of your life.

- Leticia Wharton

Master your own mind or else your mind will master you.

- Filip Slusarczyk

When two people chase a dream, they are forever connected. They will always have the journey to remember.

- Anthony C. Gruppo

You have the ability to self-adjust, therefore
you have the potential to continually self-improve.

- Anthony C. Gruppo

You may not understand what someone said,
but you will understand what their actions meant.

- Anthony C. Gruppo

Your workplace intuition is a valuable skill
when assessing a situation.

- Anthony C. Gruppo

A gentle aggressiveness may be required to
free the mind of its attempt to settle for average.

- Anthony C. Gruppo

A hardened heart does not help when making hard decisions.
A gentle calm is the best partner.

- Anthony C. Gruppo

Avoid speculating on what someone else will do.
Focus on activating what you need to do.

- Anthony C. Gruppo

Both those who challenge us, and those who care about us, are our inspiration. The challengers help us to see our flaws, and those who care about us, help us to see our strengths.

- Anthony C. Gruppo

By now you should have forgotten what annoyed you yesterday.

- Anthony C. Gruppo

Circle of life can feel like a box to the caregiver.
We need to be there to honor those who cared for us.

- Anthony C. Gruppo

Confident leaders never shutdown anyone.
They welcome every opinion. Even from their adversaries.
It is a gentle fearlessness.

- Anthony C. Gruppo

Is worrying about what to do the next day affecting your sleep? Delegate three of those tasks. People want to help. Let them.

- Anthony C. Gruppo

Dedicate a month to a person you care about.
Let them know. Now you are achieving for the both of you.

- Anthony C. Gruppo

Even the toughest shed a tear.
They know raw emotion ignites a powerful internal motion.

- Anthony C. Gruppo

Every leader knows that inside each risk lies a prayer.

- Anthony C. Gruppo

Factor failure into the plan, then it is a bridge and not a barrier.

- Anthony C. Gruppo

Your creative potential is as deep as the well
of your imagination.

- Anne Scottlin

It is not only about your educational degree,
but the degree of your courage.

- Anthony C. Gruppo

We all own a free thinking mind capable of
choosing our own destiny.

- Filip Slusarczyk

A moment of reflection generates a lifetime of momentum.

- Anthony C. Gruppo

Perhaps the purest form of motivation is making changes
for someone you love without being asked.

- Anthony C. Gruppo

Loved ones are the lining of our soul.

- Anthony C. Gruppo

Believing it will happen is the first step toward
making it happen.
Align your vision with your natural abilities and passions.

- Anthony C. Gruppo

Our flaws are merely rocky ledges to gain a
foothold on the climb to greatness.

- Anthony C. Gruppo

Reflect: What weakness have you turned into strengths?

Fear is like a prison of the mind where your dreams go to serve a sentence. Courage is your lock pick.

- Anthony C. Gruppo

Reflect: Ask yourself, what is it about this situation that I fear? What is the worst thing that can happen? Is it really that bad?

The moment you feel the need to break away from the pack and take risk, is when you are your most creative and courageous self.

- Anthony C. Gruppo

Basing beliefs on facts and reality is powerful and true; basing them on speculation and assumptions is misleading.

- Nina C. Helms

Reflect: Is there a belief you hold that you can revise around truth and factual basis?

Visioning is reflecting on both where we are going and
what we will do when we get there.

- Anthony C. Gruppo

So much more fun to push yourself
than to be pulled by someone.

- Anthony C. Gruppo

When we refuse to become complacent
our Comfort Zone evaporates.

- Anthony C. Gruppo

The pressure of leadership is sometimes the closest we come to breaking our own heart. Be so passionate about your performance others can feel the heartbeat of success emanating from you.

- Anthony C. Gruppo

Be the reason others wake up and not give up.

- Anthony C. Gruppo

Your imagination is all the inspiration you need.

- Anthony C. Gruppo

You can become the main character
in one of the most beautiful stories ever told.

- Anthony C. Gruppo

From Construction Worker to CEO
Anthony C. Gruppo

As a former college dropout and construction worker, Anthony once believed his future was without destiny. You may be feeling the same. He would suggest instead, that today you believe in your ability to achieve what yesterday you thought was impossible.

Anthony is a CEO, visionary leader, dynamic presenter, author and motivator, who challenges everyone to think in new and powerful ways.

His writings are guides for changing your destiny, creating your reality, achieving your goals and serving others. If he can transition from construction worker to CEO, you can as well in your chosen profession. As long as you continue dreaming, your path will never end. He would be honored if, through his books, you would allow him to travel along with you on your path to greatness.

Notable books by Anthony include:
- Six Degrees of Impact: Breaking Corporate Glass
- Creating Six Degrees - The Journal
- Creating Reality - A Guide to Personal Accomplishment
- Under Construction - Welding Your Passion to Your Performance

Twitter: @anthonycgruppo

Email: Anthonygruppo@yahoo.com

Website: www.Anthonygruppo.com

Instagram: www.instagram.com/acgruppo/

Linkedin: Anthony C. Gruppo

Karen Mayo

Author, entrepreneur and integrative nutrition executive health coach Karen Mayo has a passion for improving the physical and mental health of everyone she meets. Along her life's journey, Karen has kept her family roots integral to her practice.

She founded a private health coaching practice specializing in effective diet and lifestyle changes. Her goal is to increase your confidence in all aspects of life in addition to leading corporate workshops on nutrition and lifestyle for health and vitality. Karen spoke at a TEDx event and served as a guest on the Dr. Oz show.

Notable work by Karen includes Mindful Eating: Thirty Days to a Whole New You.

Twitter: @KarenMayoo

Email: coach@karenmayo.net

Website: www.karenmayo.com

Made in the USA
Middletown, DE
29 October 2023

41493345R00197